Kip the

by **William O'Connor**   illustrated by **Jim Durk**

Harcourt

Orlando   Boston   Dallas   Chicago   San Diego

Visit *The Learning Site!*

www.harcourtschool.com

ISBN 0-15-325420-3

3 4 5 6 7 8 9 10 551 10 09 08 07 06 05 04 03 02

Ordering Options
ISBN 0-15-323766-X (Collection)
ISBN 0-15-329539-2 (package of 5)

What can Kip do?

Kip can go.

Kip can hit.

Kip can dig.

Kip can pat.

Kip can tap.

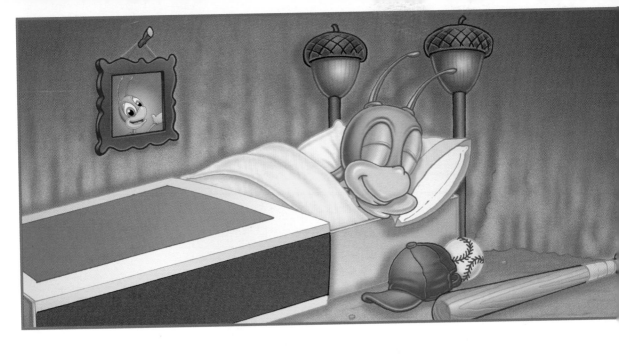

Kip can nap!